The Jolly Ocean

By Jane Singhal

Illustrated by Annie Bakst

Visit her at: anniebakststudio.com

Hardcover: 978-0-9705690-5-9
Paperback: 978-0-9705690-6-6
Ebook: 978-0-9705690-4-2

[1. Children's Book ages 3-5   2. Animals/Marine Life   3. Imagination and Play]

Published by Jane Singhal
singinghouse.com

To all who love the ocean

In the early morning sun

the jolly Ocean rolls over
on its blue tummy

and begins its merry play.

It smiles at colorful anemones

winks at rocking seahorses

and giggles at a pufferfish.

It laughs at an octopus
in disguise

and waves to barnacles

riding by.

The jolly Ocean plays chase
with a school of fish

and hide and seek
with sea crabs.

It paddles with
a sea turtle

cruises with a sting ray

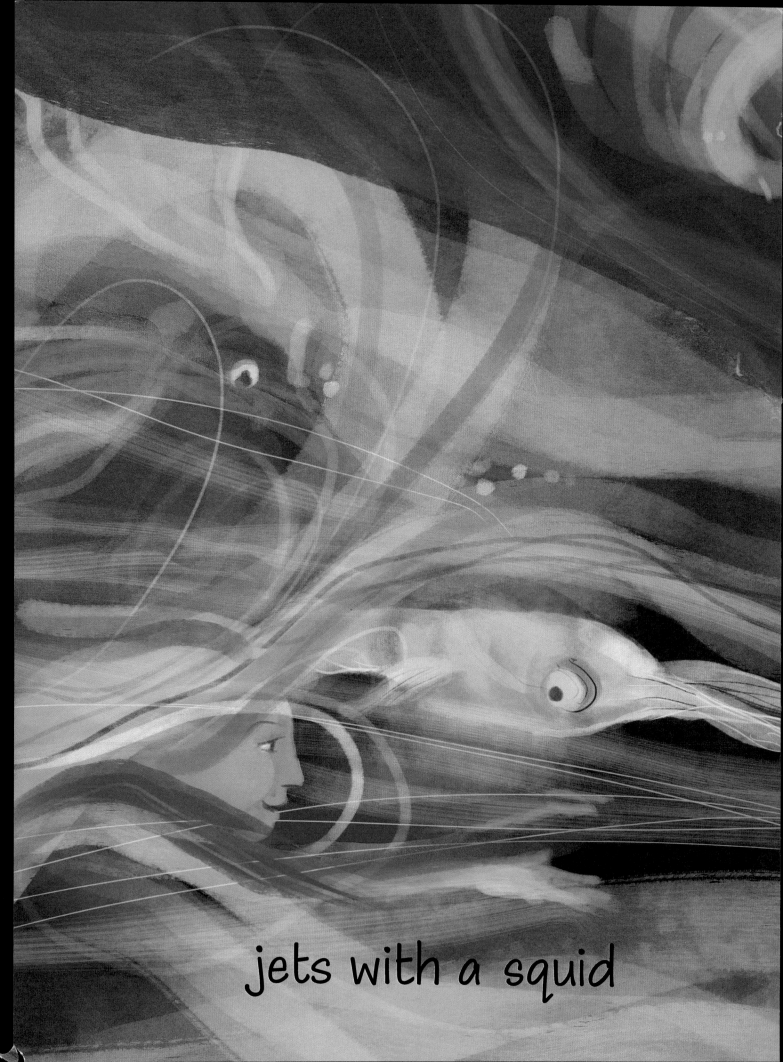

jets with a squid

plunges with otters

and flips with dolphins.

It sings a song with the whales

claps along in delight

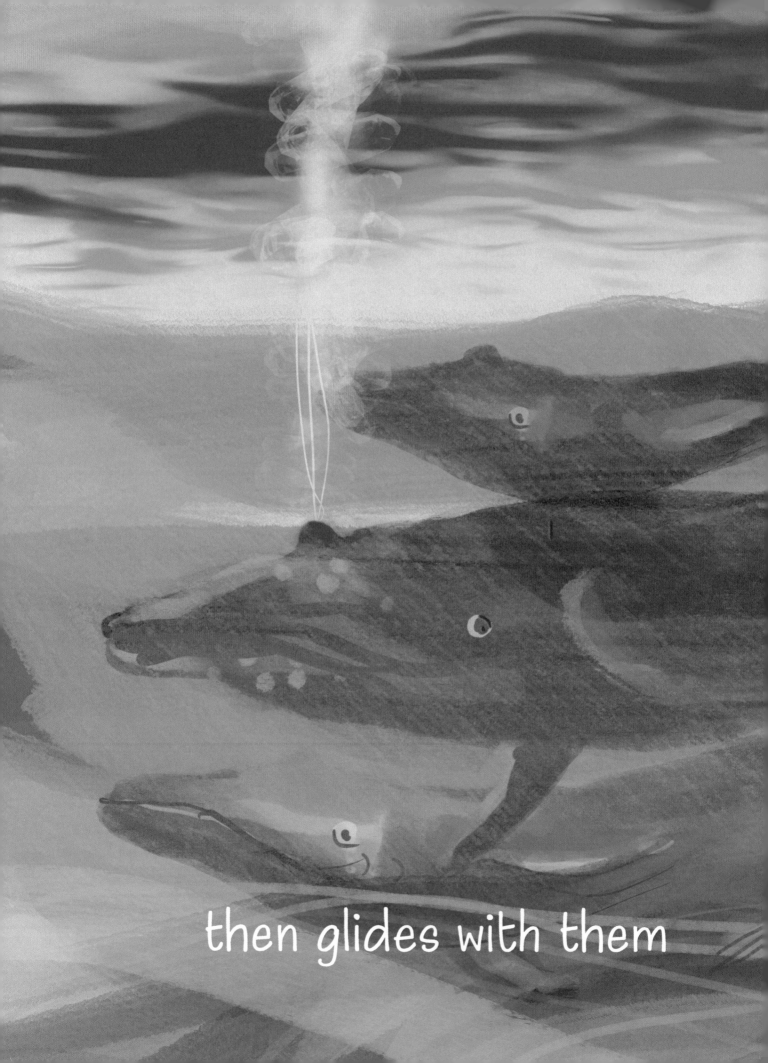

then glides with them

back to their pod.

In the early evening shadows

the jolly Ocean rolls over
and rests

after a day of fun
in its sandbox.

Lulled to sleep by
fluttering kelp leaves

it dreams of tiny starfish

and moon jellies.

Jane Singhal is a violinist from Belmont, California. She is the author of the books R*ed Light, Stop!* and *Creature Feature-A Musical Menagerie*, and creator of the CDs *Miss Jane's Children* and *Classical Tales*, all of which grew out of her years teaching music to children.

Jane and her husband live twenty minutes from the exuberant California Pacific, the source of inspiration for *The Jolly Ocean*. To learn more, visit singinghouse.com.

Annie Bakst is an illustrator and designer living in Vermont. The Vermont landscape has inspired the joy of color and shapes and textures of the natural world.

She has illustrated two graphic novels, children's books, many murals for a children's hospital, and has had several gallery shows. She has won numerous national design awards and a Society of Illustrators Award in NYC. Visit anniebakststudio.com

Made in the USA
Middletown, DE
21 December 2021

56814312R00020